Eid Songs

by
Fawzia Gillani

Goodwordkidz
Helping you build a family of faith

Call on Allah

Early in the morning,
Late at night,
We call on Allah to make things right,
We ask for protection,
We know He has Might,
We want His affection,
For every day and night.

Ramadhan's Here

The month is here, please take cheer,
Ramadhan, Ramadhan, Ramadhan's here,
A time to fast and give *zakah*,
Worship Allah and make *dua*,
All the devils are chained these days,
Build your faith and better your ways.

Little Pretty Sumayah

Little pretty Sumayah,
Forgot to do her *niyyah*,
Now her fast won't count,
She said, "Please remind me,
Shaitan's trying to find me!
I'll try and figure it out.
Now, pretty little Sumaya,
Will always do her *niyyah*,
And her fast will count!

Aminah Aminah

Aminah, Aminah what do you wear?
I wear a *khimar* to cover my hair.
Aminah, Aminah why is it so?
Allah says, your hair should not show.
Aminah, Aminah why do you pray?
I promised Allah five times a day.
Aminah, Aminah why do you fast?
To strengthen my soul, and clean sins of my past.
Amina, Amina why do you weep?
I pray my Lord my soul will keep.

There Were Ten In The Gang

There were ten in the gang and the little one sang,
'Time for prayer, time for prayer.'
So one went out to do *wudu*.
There were nine in the gang and the little one sang,
'Time for prayer, time for prayer.'
So one went out to do *wudu*.
There were eight in the gang and the little one sang,
'Time for prayer, time for prayer.'
So one went out to do *wudu*.
There were seven in the gang and the little one sang,
'Time for prayer, time for prayer.'
So one went out to do wudu.
There were six in the gang and the little one sang,
'Time for prayer, time for prayer.'
So one went out to do wudu.
There were five in the gang and the little one sang,
'Time for prayer, time for prayer.'
So one went out to do wudu.

There were five in the gang and the little one sang,
'Time for prayer, time for prayer.'
So one went out to do wudu.
There were four in the gang and the little one sang,
'Time for prayer, time for prayer.'
So one went out to do wudu.
There were three in the gang and the little one sang,
'Time for prayer, time for prayer.'
So one went out to do wudu.
There were two in the gang and the little one sang,
'Time for prayer, time for prayer.'
So one went out to do wudu.
There was one in the gang and the little one sang
'Time for prayer, time for prayer.'
So he went out to do wudu.
There were ten in the gang and the little one sang,
Qad qamatis salah, qad qamatis salah.

My Friends

When all of my friends play in the sun,
I like to count them one by one,
The first is Gabe so kind and neat,
The second is Yunus so clean and sweet,
The third is Salih who feeds the poor,
The fourth is Adam who cleans the mosque door,
When all of my friends play in the sun,
I like to count them one by one.

Five Busy Honey Bees

Five busy honey bees resting in the sun,
One went home, his work was done!
Four busy honey bees resting in the sun,
One said 'Ya Allah! I never have fun.'
Three busy honey bees resting in the sun,
One said 'Bismillah'. My work have begun,
Two busy honey bees resting in the sun,
One said, '*Masha Allah*, I have won!'
One busy honey bee resting in the sun,
Says 'La ilaha illallah, God is One.'

What could it be?

Samoseh and kebabs,
Sisters in *hijabs*,
What could it be?
The imam is in his robe,
Brothers in their *thobe*,
What could it be?
Cookies in a tin,
Children looking prim,
What could it be?
Balloons in the hallway,
Ribbons getting in the way,
What could it be?
Laughing in the houses,
Smiles in the streets,
What could it be?

Tippy Tippy Tiptar

Tippy tippy tiptar, first day of *iftar*,
What do I take to the mosque?
A plate of rice and a pinch of spice,
That's what you take to the mosque.

Tippy tippy tiptar, second day of *iftar*,
What do I take to the mosque?
A bunch of dates, on a pretty plate,
That's what you take to the mosque.

Tippy tippy tiptar, third day of *iftar*,
What do I take to the mosque?
A lemon cake that Ama did bake,
That's what you take to the mosque.

Tippy tippy tiptar, fourth day of *iftar*,
What do I take to the mosque?
Samoseh in a tin, apples in a bin,
That's what you take to the mosque.

Tippy tippy tiptar, every day of *iftar*,
What do I take to the mosque?
I'll take a good measure, earn Allah's pleasure,
That's what you take to the mosque.

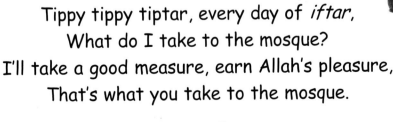

Clip Clip Clippity - Clippity Clop

Clip clip clippity - clippity clop,
Here comes mother with her brand new mop,
Splish over here, splash over there,
Cleaning, scrubbing everywhere,
Dusting all the cobwebs, beating all the mats,
Arranging all the furniture, hanging all the hats
Mother dear, please tell me - who is coming here?
She said my son, don't you know ? Eid-ul-Fitr's near!

Eid Mubarak

Eid mubarak to you and you,
Eid kareem for you and for you,
Everyone's happy to share in the fun,
Everyone's happy that Eid has begun.

One Little Orphan

One little orphan wanted to eat,
I rushed to the shop and bought him a treat,
He said, 'dear brother, thank you so,
There's something that I want you to know:
Allah is one, He is so kind,
He wants you to say your *Fajr* on time,
Read the Qur'an and your mother obey,
And listen to your teacher every day.

La Ilaha Illallah

La ilaha illallah Muhammadur rasoolullah,
A claim of faith for you and me,
Let's all practice honesty,
La ilaha illallah Muhammadur rasoolullah,
Eid is here, let's have some fun,
Let's invite everyone,
La ilaha illallah Muhammadur rasoolullah.

Eid, Eid is a Family Time

Eid, Eid is a family time,
Everyone's together to laugh and dine,
Balloons and ribbons and sparkles everywhere,
Mothers and fathers, uncles and aunts,
Brothers and sisters, cousins with plants,
Here comes grandpa to give out some treats,
He gives out Eidi to everyone he meets,
To Fatima and Zahra, to Ali and John,
Eid, Eid is a family time,
Everyone's together to laugh and to dine.

Three Eight Seven

Three, eight, seven,
I want to go to heaven,
Pow, pow, pow,
Can you tell me how?
Ya, ya, ya,
This is how,
Sa, sa ,sa,
Do your *Salah*,
Ba, ba, ba,
Pay your *Zakah*,
Fa, fa, fa,
Make sure you fast,
Ja, ja, ja,
Make for the *Hajj*.

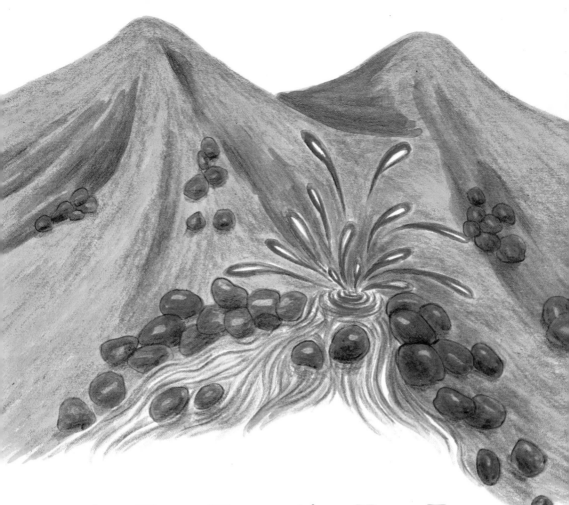

Abe Zum Zum, Abe Zum Zum

Abe Zum Zum, Abe Zum Zum,
Always run run,
Always run run,
Abe Zum Zum, Abe Zum Zum,
Gift for Hajar's son, son,
Hajar's son, son,
Abe Zum Zum, Abe Zum Zum,
Cool for every one, one,
Every one, one,
Abe Zum Zum, Abe Zum Zum.

Once in a Lifetime

Once in a lifetime I will go,
I will be a pilgrim, my faith will grow,
Pay all my debts, redress my wrongs,
Return all things to whom they belong,
Take all my luggage, a purse of money,
To pay for the hotel, the milk and honey.

Once in a lifetime I will go,
I will be a pilgrim, my faith will grow,
Round and round the Kabah I will run,
And I won't mind the shining sun,
Off to Mina and then Arafat,
This is a plain so wide and flat.

Farmer O Farmer

Farmer, O farmer, I need a good goat,
Umar, O Umar, why a good goat?
For the *Eid of Adha*, blessed is it,
A time to give meat to the poor and the fit,
A time to remember Khaleel of Allah,
He was obedient and brave and did his *Salah*.

Round the Kabah We Go

Round and round and round we go,
Round the Kabah, slow and slow,
We all ask Allah to cleanse our sins,
Forgive our wrongs and *jannah* win,
All the time our faith will grow,
Praising Allah in a row,
Round and round and round we go,
Round the Kabah, slow and slow.

Omar Wears His *Kufi*

Omar wears his *kufi*,
He's such a handsome boy,
He bought his mom a ruby,
He bought his dad a toy,
Everywhere where Omar goes,
He wears his *kufi* there,
Today his father said to him,
'Look son, I really care.
'Here is a gift for you, I'll put it on your chair.'
As Omar turned around to look, he saw a *kufi* there,
He smiled and said *masha Allah*, now I have a pair!

Thank Allah

Hands to your ears,
Hands by our sides,
Turning to the Kabah,
To Allah we pray.
We thank Him for Eid,
We thank Him for the day ,
We thank Him for everything He passes our way.

Glossary

Bismillah : To begin in the name of Allah

Dua : Supplication

Eidi : Gifts given to the children on Eid

Eid Mubark : Happy Eid

Fajr : Dawn Prayer

Hajar : The Prophet Ismail's Mother

Hajj : Pilgrimage to Makkah

Hijab : a Head scarf or a veil

Iftar : Breaking of Fast in the evening

Jannah: Paradise

Kabah : the House of Allah in Makkah

Khaleel of Allah : The Prophet Ibrahim ﷺ

Khimar : Head scarf

Kufi : Cap

La ilaha illallah : There is no god but Allah

La ilaha illallah Muhammadur Rasoolullah: There is no god but Allah and Muhammad ﷺ is His prophet and servant

Masha Allah : When we praise we say Masha Allah, which means 'If Allah wills'

Niyyah : Intention

Salah : Five daily prayers

Thobe : Robe

Wudu : Ablution

Zakah : Almsgiving

Zum Zum : Water of Zum Zum, a spring found in Makkah